W9-CAF-061

Littlest
Pet Shop
TM

WAIT A
SECOND

HC: 978-1-63140-359-0 • TPB: 978-1-63140-429-0

18 17 16 15 1 2 3 4

Licensed By: Hasbro

www.IDWPUBLISHING.com
IDW founded by Ted Adams, Alex Garner, Kris Oprisko, and Robbie Robbins

Facebook: facebook.com/idwpublishing
Twitter: @idwpublishing
YouTube: youtube.com/idwpublishing
Instagram: instagram.com/idwpublishing
deviantART: idwpublishing.deviantart.com
Pinterest: pinterest.com/idwpublishing/idw-staff-faves

Originally published in LITTLEST PET SHOP issues #1–5 and as LITTLEST PET SHOP: SPRING CLEANING!

art by Nicanor Peña, Colors by Victoria Robado

The Old Switcheroo
Written by GEORGIA BALL
Art by NICANOR PEÑA
Colors by VICTORIA ROBADO
Letters by GILBERTO LAZCANO
WHERE— WHERE AM I...?
WELCOME TO SHADY BROOKS, PEPPER CLARK...
WE HOPE YOU ENJOY YOUR STAY...
YOUR... LONG, EXTENDED STAY...
"PLEASANT DREAMS!"
GAAAASP!!!

NEXT MORNING, AT THE LITTLEST PET SHOP...
—AND THEN THEY LOCKED ME UP AND THREW AWAY THE KEY! IT WAS A NIGHTMARE.
THAT SOUNDS AWFUL.
DON'T GET ALL WORKED UP OVER A DREAM, PEPPER. OVERNIGHT BOARDING IS GREAT!
YOU'VE ONLY STAYED OVERNIGHT AT LITTLEST PET SHOP, RUSSELL.
I'VE HEARD SHADY BROOKS IS REALLY NICE. THEY HAVE TONS OF GOOD REVIEWS ONLINE.
OF COURSE THEY HAVE GOOD REVIEWS. THAT'S HOW THEY GET YOU.
WHAT DOES THAT EVEN MEAN?
I DON'T UNDERSTAND WHY MY OWNER IS GOING ON A BUSINESS TRIP THE ONE WEEK MRS. TWOMBLY CAN'T TAKE ME.
DOESN'T HE KNOW HIS LIFE IS SUPPOSED TO REVOVLVE AROUND ME??
I'LL BE RIGHT BACK!

MY TASTE TEST IS HERE!
IS THAT THE ONE WHERE YOU TRY OUT TWO DISGUSTING FLAVORS OF POWDERED LIZARD FOOD?
WHEN YOU PUT IT LIKE THAT, IT SOUNDS REALLY GROSS.
YECH! THE ONLY THING WORSE THAN EATING FLIES IS EATING MYSTERY JARS OF POWDER THAT VAGUELY TASTE LIKE FLIES.
I UNDERSTAND HOW YOU FEEL, PEPPER. I WOULD BE SAD IF MY OWNER WENT AWAY, NO MATTER *WHERE* I WAS BOARDED.
YOUR WORRIES ARE OVER! MRS. TWOMBLY AND I MADE A FEW CALLS...
...AND WE'VE ARRANGED FOR YOU TO STAY WITH PENNY LING THIS WEEK!
OOO! BLYTHE! THANK YOU— THANK YOU— THANK YOU!!
ISN'T THAT FANTASTIC, PENNY?
YEAH... FANTASTIC.

THAT NIGHT AT PENNY LING'S HOUSE...
PENNY
IT'S SIX O'CLOCK! PEPPER WILL BE HERE ANY MINUTE.
IT'S NOT THAT I DON'T WANT TO SEE HER... IT'S JUST THAT I'M USED TO HAVING THINGS AT HOME BE A CERTAIN WAY...
HEY, PENNY LING! I BROUGHT A FEW THINGS, HOPE YOU HAVE ROOM.
OH! THAT'S... A LOT.
BEFORE YOU GET SETTLED WE SHOULD GO OVER THE HOUSE RULES. AT THIS TIME OF NIGHT I USUALLY—
JUST LOOK AT THIS PLACE! I HAD NO IDEA YOUR HOUSE WAS SO *FUN*.
YOU HAVE YOUR OWN TIRE SWING!
YES, BUT IT'S A LITTLE TOO LATE TO USE IT—
ARE THESE YOUR CLOTHES? YOU *HAVE* TO LET ME BORROW YOUR CLOTHES.
I... I DON'T THINK THEY'LL FIT YOU VERY WELL...

WHAT'S THAT?
IT BELONGS TO MR. PETTUS! HE'D BE HEARTBROKEN IF SOMETHING HAPPENED TO IT.
RELAX, PENNY. I'LL BE CAREFUL.
OOO, IS THAT YOUR *BED*?
ON'T YOU THINK WE HOULD, YOU OW, TRY TO IND DOWN FOR THE EVENING?
I HAVE TO WIND MYSELF UP BEFORE I CAN WIND DOWN.
SIGH
THIS IS GOING TO BE HARDER THAN I THOUGHT.
NNY

"I JUST KNOW THE STRESS IS GOING TO GIVE ME WEIRD DREAMS..."
I CAN'T WAIT TO SPEND THE NIGHT SNUGGLED UP IN FRONT OF MY FAVORITE SHOWS...
I'M HOME, ROOMIE!
HA HA HA HA HA HA HA
I INVITED SOME FRIENDS OVER FOR PIZZA. THAT'S COOL, RIGHT?
IT'S NOT "COOL"! I AM NOT DRESSED FOR COMPANY.
HA HA HA HA HA
THAT'S OK, WE DON'T MIND.
HA HA HA HA HA
WILL SOMEONE TURN OFF THE LAUGHTRACK ON THIS SITCOM?!
HA HA HA
SNRK
SNERK
SNOOOOORK
HONK SHOOO
HONK
GRRR..

HE NEXT MORNING...
"USE THE FORM PROVIDED TO TELL US WHICH FLAVOR YOUR PET PREFERS...
"AND YOUR FEEDBACK WILL HELP SHAPE OUR NEWEST LINE OF LIZARD FEED!"
HMMM...
THE SUSPENSE IS KILLING ME.
I CAN'T TAKE THIS LIGHTLY, SUNIL. THE FUTURE OF IGUANA FOOD IS AT STAKE.
YOU LOOK A LITTLE TIRED, PENNY. ARE YOU ALL RIGHT?
OH YES, I'M—*YAWN*
SIGH NO, I'M NOT ALL RIGHT.

I LOVE SEEING PEPPER EVERY DAY, SHE'S A REALLY GOOD FRIEND.
I'M JUST NOT SURE I WANT TO SEE HER EVERY DAY *AND* EVERY NIGHT.
AND THAT MAKES ME A REALLY BAD FRIEND, DOESN'T IT?
YOU'RE A GREAT FRIEND! YOU'RE JUST A LITTLE OUT OF YOUR COMFORT ZONE.
TRY TO RELAX A LITTLE. LET THINGS GO. BE MORE LIKE...
WELL, MORE LIKE PEPPER!
—AND IF I EAT PICKLES AND MAYONNAISE AT THE SAME TIME I CAN MAKE THE ROOM SMELL LIKE A BLT!
OR MAYBE NOT.
NO, RUSSELL. YOU'RE RIGHT.
PEPPER WOULD *WANT* ME TO LOOSEN UP.

TER THAT NIGHT...
PENNY? I'M HERE!
WHERE—
AHHHHHH!!!
BOOGIE BOOGIE BOOGIE!
ARE YOU PLAYING WITH YOUR OWNER'S MASK? BECAUSE YOU SAID HE'D GET REALLY UPSET.
HE SURE WILL!
NO BIGGIE, RIGHT?
WHOAH!
IT'S LIKE YOU ALWAYS SAY, PEPPER... LIVE A LITTLE!
I HAVE A HUGE LIST OF THINGS FOR US TO DO TONIGHT. FIRST WE'LL GET INTO THE LAUNDRY AND HIDE THE SOCKS, AND THEN WE'LL RAID THE FRIDGE AND EAT ALL OF THE YOGURT—
HEH-HEH, YEAH, BUT WON'T STUFF LIKE THAT GET US IN TROUBLE?
WELL, YEAH... A LITTLE.

THE NEXT DAY...
—AND SHE WOULDN'T LET ME GO TO SLEEP UNTIL WE'D SHOT AN ENTIRE BAG OF RUBBER BANDS AT HER OWNER'S COLLECTION OF CERAMIC TIGERS!
AN ENTIRE BAG, MINKA.
SOUNDS LIKE A REGULAR TUESDAY NIGHT TO ME.
IT'S ALL FUN AND GAMES UNTIL THE HOUSEGUEST GETS THROWN OUT FOR BA BEHAVIOR.
THAT DOESN'T SOUND LIKE PENNY.
I'M SURE IT'S NOT AS BAD AS YOU THINK.
IT'S WORSE THAN YOU THINK.
WAIT, IS SHE... TELLING A JOKE?
IF PENNY LING ISN'T GOING TO DO IT, YOU'LL HAVE TO BE THE RESPONSIBLE PET HERE.
HA HA HA—GOOD ONE, ZOE.
OH. YOU WERE SERIOUS.

OF *COURSE* I WAS SERIOUS. YOU'LL HAVE TO BE MORE CAREFUL, MORE RESPECTFUL, LESS...
WELL, YOU KNOW...

LESS "PEPPER."
NOT THAT WE DON'T *LOVE* "PEPPER."

THIS REMINDS ME OF A MOVIE I SAW ONE TIME...

HEY! I TRIED TO DRESS LIKE YOU BUT NOW YOU'RE DRESSED LIKE ME BEFORE I DRESSED LIKE YOU.
THAT'S AWKWARD! LET'S HAVE A MUSICAL NUMBER AND PRETEND ALL OF OUR DIFFERENCES ARE RESOLVED.

HOW DID THE MOVIE END?
I DON'T REMEMBER. VINNIE BET HE COULD GET MORE WET JELLY BEANS TO STICK TO THE SCREEN THAN I COULD.
I KIND OF GOT DISTRACTED.
WELL, YOU KNOW WHAT I REMEMBER ABOUT THAT MOVIE?
IT HAD A *MAKEOVER*!
MAKEOVER TIME!!!
WE'VE TRIED THIS BEFORE—SERIOUSLY HAS IT EVER WORKED?
IT'S MORE ABOUT THE JOURNEY THAN THE DESTINATION.

WHILE...
HMM...
ELL?
DRY, WITH FLORAL NOTES AND A SUBTLE HINT OF GRASS.
THAT IS A NICE WAYING OF SAYING IT TASTES LIKE OMETHING YOU UG UP IN THE GARDEN.
NOT HELPING, SUNIL. PET LIZARDS EVERYWHERE ARE COUNTING ON ME!
I THINK WE ALL NEED TO COME TOGETHER AND SUPPORT VINNIE DURING THIS DIFFICULT TIME.
UH...
THAT'S A REALLY SENSITIVE THING TO SAY, PEPPER.
ARE YOU RE YOU'RE FEELING OK?
PSST!
FLIPPITY
FLIPPITY
FLIPPIT
GULP

I'M JUST GOING TO BACK AWAY FOR NO SPECIAL REASON—
HEY, WHAT DO YOU CALL AN IGUANA WHO CAN'T MAKE UP HIS MIND? A DIZZY LIZZY!
AHH! PENNY JUST MADE A TERRIBLE PUN! I DON'T KNOW WHO YOU GUYS ARE ANYMORE!
YOU SHOULDN'T BE GOOFING AROUND, YOUR FRIEND IS UPSET.
WHEN DID YOU TURN INTO SUCH A KILLJOY?
THE SAME TIME YOU STOPPED BEING RESPONSIBLE.
I LIKED THE OLD, FUN AND JOKEY PEPPER.
WELL, I MISS THE SWEET AND NICE PENNY LING.
YOU DO? I THOUGHT THAT YOU THOUGHT I WAS TOO UPTIGHT.
I THOUGHT YOU THOUGHT I WAS TOO LOUD AND ROUGH TO STAY AT YOUR HOUSE.

WELL, YOU HAVEN'T BEEN VERY CAREFUL WITH MY THINGS... AND I *AM* USED TO MY ROUTINE
UT I HAVE JOYED YOUR COMPANY, PEPPER.
I SHOULD HAVE PAID MORE ATTENTION TO THE HOUSE RULES.
I WAS JUST HAVING A REALLY GOOD TIME STAYING OVER!
I DON'T WANT YOU TO CHANGE TO MAKE ME HAPPY. I'M SORRY.
I'M SORRY TOO. I DO NEED TO BE A LITTLE FLEXIBLE, YOU'RE MY GUEST!
DOES THAT MEAN YOU'LL STOP WAVING THAT RIBBON AROUND? BECAUSE IT'S KIND OF FREAKING ME OUT.
AS SOON AS POSSIBLE.
OVERS EPPER VER CK.
YBE I LD GIVE ONE ETIME, NKA...
TOO LATE!

I'M READY TO HELP YOU SEND IN YOUR FORM, VINNIE. WHICH FLAVOR DID YOU PICK?
WELL, FLAVOR "A" HAD... UH... BUT FLAVOR "B" HAD... WELL...
TO TELL YOU THE TRUTH, THEY BOTH TASTED LIKE SPACKLE.
"NEITHER" IT IS.
YOU KNOW, I'M KIND OF SORRY YOU'RE ONLY STAYING ONE MORE NIGHT.
I'M SO RELIEVED YOU SAID THAT! MY OWNER NEEDS TO STAY ANOTHER WEEK.
I WAS GOING TO BOARD WITH MRS. TWOMBLY, BUT NOW I CAN JUST STAY WITH YOU.
ULP!
I'M KIDDING, BUT YOUR FACE! *HILARIOUS*!
I'M GLAD YOU'RE BACK TO YOUR OLD SELF. I'VE BEEN WAITING UNTIL YOU WERE IN A GOOD MOOD TO TELL YOU WHAT'S IN THE PUDDING MR. PETTUS FEEDS US.
UH, WHAT'S IN THE—OH! YOU GOT ME. GOOD ONE, PENNY.
YEAH, I WAS JUST JOKING.
MAYBE.

WANT TO JOIN US IN A ROUSING GAME OF "GO FISH," BLYTHE? IT'S FULL OF THRILLS!
WHATEVER YOU SAY SUNIL
Written by GEORGIA BALL
Art by ANTONIO CAMPO
Colors by DIEGO RODRIGUEZ
Letters by GILBERTO LAZCANO
NO TIME TODAY, RUSSELL.
I NEED TO FINISH MY APPLICATION FOR THE DOWNTOWN UNIVERSITY FASHION WEEK PROGRAM.
NOT SURE WHAT I'LL DO WITH MY SPRING BREAK IF I DON'T GET IN.
I DESPAIR OF REACHING THIS ITCH ON MY OWN.
MINKA, COULD YOU PASS ME THE BACK SCRATCHER?
MINKA? IT'S RIGHT BESIDE YOU.
MINKA? *MINKA!*
OH, HEY SUNIL! DID YOU NEED SOMETHING?
ARRGH! MINKA, YOU NEVER LISTEN.

SOMETIMES I WISH I COULD JUST HYPNOTIZE YOU LONG ENOUGH TO MAKE YOU PAY ATTENTION TO ME!
SPROING
SUNIL, I AM AT YOUR COMMAND.
ON ALL THAT IS IMPOSSIBLE, IT ACTUALLY WORKED.
ALLOW ME TO SCRATCH YOUR BACK, SUNIL.
I CERTAINLY WILL NOT ARGUE.
WHAT ELSE WOULD YOU HAVE ME DO, SUNIL?
WELL, I WOULDN'T MIND HAVING A LITTLE FRUIT.
WHOOSH
IS THIS ENOUGH FRUIT, SUNIL?
KEEP IT COMING, I'LL LET YOU KNOW.

BURP WHO KNEW
RS. TWOMBLY EVEN HAD THAT MANY GRAPES?
WHAT CAN I DO FOR YOU NEXT, SUNIL?
OH! UH, I'M GOOD FOR NOW, THANKS.
I AM HERE TO SERVE YOUR WISHES.
BUT I DON'T HAVE ANY WISHES AT THE MOMENT. ISN'T THERE SOMETHING YOU WOULD LIKE TO DO FOR YOURSELF?
MY ONLY PURPOSE IS TO DO WHAT YOU COMMAND.
GRRR...
WHAT IS YOUR COMMAND, SUNIL?
CAN I GET YOU ANYTHING, SUNIL?
MAGICIAN
WHAT CAN I DO FOR YOU, SUNIL?

ARRRGH!
I DON'T *WANT* TO TELL YOU WHAT TO DO ALL THE TIME! I WISH I HAD NEVER HYPNOTIZED YOU.
?!
I KNOW. I JUST WANTED TO HEAR YOU SAY IT.
BUT I THOUGHT YOU WERE HYPNOTIZED!
NAW. I WAS JUST PRETENDING.
I CAN'T TELL YOU HOW RELIEVED I AM THAT IT DIDN'T WORK. ORDERING SOMEONE AROUND IS A TERRIBLE RESPONSIBILITY.
SUNIL...
SUNIL...
WHAT DO YOU COMMAND, SUNIL?
End.

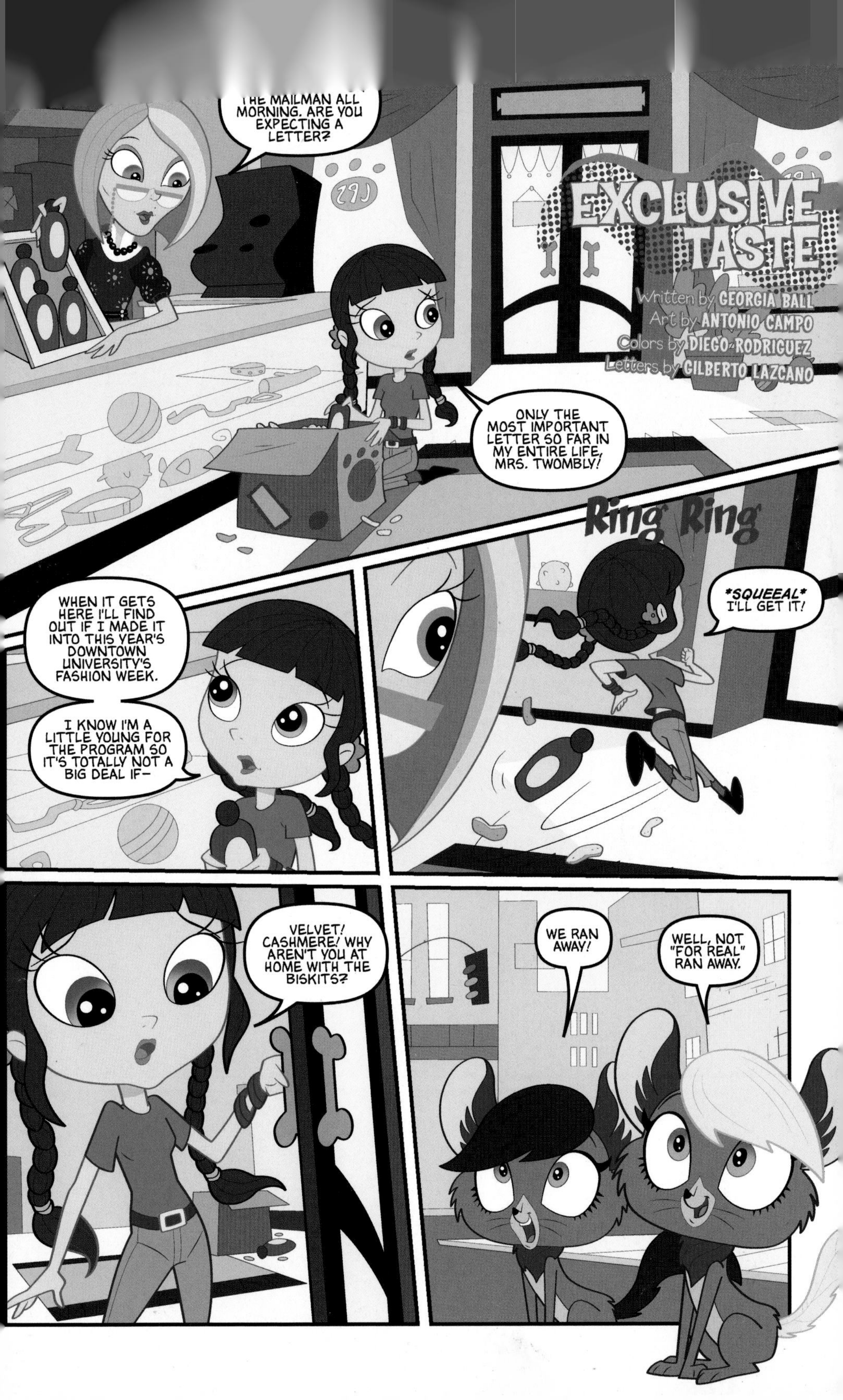
THE MAILMAN ALL MORNING. ARE YOU EXPECTING A LETTER?
EXCLUSIVE TASTE
Written by GEORGIA BALL
Art by ANTONIO CAMPO
Colors by DIEGO RODRIGUEZ
Letters by GILBERTO LAZCANO
ONLY THE MOST IMPORTANT LETTER SO FAR IN MY ENTIRE LIFE, MRS. TWOMBLY!
Ring Ring
WHEN IT GETS HERE I'LL FIND OUT IF I MADE IT INTO THIS YEAR'S DOWNTOWN UNIVERSITY'S FASHION WEEK.
I KNOW I'M A LITTLE YOUNG FOR THE PROGRAM SO IT'S TOTALLY NOT A BIG DEAL IF—
SQUEEAL I'LL GET IT!
VELVET! CASHMERE! WHY AREN'T YOU AT HOME WITH THE BISKITS?
WE RAN AWAY!
WELL, NOT "FOR REAL" RAN AWAY.

THIS IS THE ONLY CHANCE WE HAVE OF GETTING THE BIRTHDAY GIFT WE REALLY WANT.
"PIONEER POLLY'S ALL-NATURAL EAR LOTION."
IT'S A LITTLEST PET SHOP EXCLUSIVE.
BUT WHY COULDN'T WHITTANY AND BRITTANY BUY IT FOR YOU?
PFFT. LIKE THEY WOULD EVER SHOP HERE.
THEY DON'T UNDERSTAND US THE WAY YOU DO, BLYTHE. THEY DON'T EVEN KNOW IT'S OUR BIRTHDAY!
THAT IS TOO BAD.
PARDON ME, BUT HAVE YOU SEEN A PAIR OF VERY DIFFICULT CHINCHILLAS?
THEY'RE RIGHT HERE, FRANCOIS.
I THINK THEY WERE DRAWN INTO THE STORE BY THE SWEET SMELL OF OUR NEW EAR LOTION.
MISS BAXTER, THE TWINS ARE WORRIED SICK. ARE YOU TAKING ADVANTAGE OF THEIR MISFORTUNE TO MAKE A SALE?
IT KIND OF LOOKS LIKE THAT, DOESN'T IT...

BUT I THINK YOU WOULD UNDERSTAND IF YOU TRIED IT!
NOT ON YOUR OWN EARS, OF COURSE...
THAT WOULD BE WEIRD.
I DO APPRECIATE YOUR HELP BUT I THINK WE'LL BE ON OUR WAY.
WAIT! YOU CAN HAVE IT FOR FREE. I'LL PAY FOR IT MYSELF, JUST... *PLEASE* DON'T LEAVE WITHOUT "PIONEER POLLY."
FORGIVE ME, MISS BAXTER, BUT IF YOU HAD GROWN UP WITH CHINCHILLAS AS I DID, YOU WOULD UNDERSTAND THAT LOTION IS NOT APPROPRIATE FOR THIS KIND OF ANIMAL–
ARRGH!
WHY WON'T HE JUST *LISTEN*?
CRASH

I'M TERRIBLY SORRY, MISS. IT SEEMS I'LL BE PAYING FOR A BOTTLE AFTER ALL.
SHEA BUTTER, HONEY, VITAMIN E—HMM... NOT BAD.
EW!
YOU DIDN'T MENTION IT WAS EDIBLE, MISS BAXTER.
WELL, IT *IS* ALL-NATURAL.
CHINCHILLAS OFTEN GROOM THEMSELVES LIKE CATS. ANY LOTION WE USE ON THEM MUST BE SAFE TO EAT, LIKE THIS DELIGHTFUL PRODUCT.
I'LL TAKE A CASE OF IT.
HAPPY BIRTHDAY, YOU TWO! ISN'T THERE SOMETHING YOU WANT TO SAY IN RETURN?
OH, OF COURSE!
HOW STUPID OF US!
THANKS FOR HELPING ME SNEAK OUT, VELVET! YOUR PLAN REALLY PAID OFF.
NO, THANK *YOU*, CASHMERE. FINDING BLYTHE WAS *YOUR* IDEA.
YOU'RE WELCOME.
End

SPRING BREAK BEACH BUMMER
Written by GEORGIA BALL
Art by NICANOR PEÑA
Edits by DAVID HEDGECOCK
Colors by VICTORIA ROBADO
Letters by GILBERTO LAZCANO
IT'S HERE! MY LETTER FINALLY CAME!
AH... SEEMS LIKE ONLY YESTERDAY WHEN YOU WERE GETTING THIS EXCITED OVER A NEW PACIFIER.
DAD!
NOW YOU'RE ALL GROWN UP AND APPLYING FOR THE DOWNTOWN UNIVERSITY FASHION WEEK PROGRAM.
SO, WHAT DOES IT SAY?
I DIDN'T GET IN.

DON'T BE TOO DOWN ABOUT IT, BLYTHE. THAT PROGRAM IS USUALLY SOMETHING FOR KIDS A LITTLE OLDER THAN YOU ARE.
YOU'LL HAVE PLENTY OF CHANCES TO TRY AGAIN. WHY DON'T YOU GO BACK TO CALLIGRAPHY CAMP?
YOU'VE HAD THE BEST PEN STROKE FOR SEVEN YEARS AND COUNTING!
IT'S ALL SETTLED. SEE YOU AT DINNER!
SIGH

TWANG
SUGAR SPRINKLES!
WHAAAT'S UP... YOU LOOK LIKE YOU JUST FOUND A HOLE IN THE BOTTOM OF YOUR ICE CREAM CONE.
TRIED OUT FOR A SPRING BREAK FASHION WEEK PROGRAM BUT I DIDN'T GET IN.
I KNEW I WAS A LITTLE INEXPERIENCED WHEN I APPLIED...
I GUESS I JUST WANTED TO FEEL OLDER. YOU KNOW, DO SOMETHING MORE ADVANCED.
MORE ADVANCED THAN CALLIGRAPHY CAMP, ANYWAY.
THAT IS A LETDOWN. BUT IT'S ALSO YOUR CHANCE TO DO SOMETHING REALLY MELLOW.
EVERYBODY KNOWS THE HOT PLACE TO HANG IS THE SCORCHING TORCH BEACH FESTIVAL.
SCORCHING TORCH BEACH FESTIVAL

OOO, I'VE HEARD OF THAT. OVERNIGHT CAMPING AND ART PROJECTS, RIGHT?
YEAH, BUT I MOSTLY GO FOR THE TUNES.
NOT SURE HOW I'D CONVINCE MY DAD TO LET ME GO TO THAT—UH OH, I'M LATE FOR WORK!
IF YOU CHANGE YOUR MIND WE'LL TOTALLY SYNC UP.
THAT AFTERNOON AT THE LITTLEST PET SHOP...
DO YOU STILL PLAN TO TAKE THE WEEK OFF, BLYTHE?
THAT DEPENDS... HAVE YOU EVER HEARD OF THE SCORCHING TORCH BEACH FESTIVAL, MRS. TWOMBLY?
HAVE I?! I USED TO GO EVERY YEAR...
...IN MY YOUNGER DAYS, OF COURSE.
WHY DON'T WE ALL GO TOGETHER? THE PETS ARE ALL STAYING WITH ME THIS WEEK ANYWAY—MOST OF THE OWNERS ARE ON VACATION.
I'LL ASK MY DAD!

ONE PARENTAL PERMISSION SLIP LATER, IT'S OFF TO DOWNTOWN CITY BEACH!
I'M GLAD THIS FESTIVAL IS PET-FRIENDLY.
LOTS OF PEOPLE BRING THEIR DOGS, SO I'M SURE THEY WON'T MIND ONE LITTLE HEDGEHOG, A MONKEY, A PANDA—
ICE CREA
ICE
WHOOPSIE!
ARTISTIC EXPRESSION COMING THROUGH!
MY MEMORIES OF THIS FESTIVAL HAVE FEWER THINGS ON FIRE.
LET'S FIND A SPOT TO SET UP CAMP.
THIS IS THE WILDEST THING I'VE EVER SEEN AND I'VE SEEN EVERY EPISODE OF "THE WILDEST THINGS EVER"!
YOU'RE TOTALLY WELCOME.
HEY!
POP
POP
OOPS!

ARE YOU SURE YOU DON'T NEED ANY HELP, MRS. TWOMBLY?
I'VE BEEN SETTING UP TENTS SINCE YOU WERE IN DIAPERS! YOU JUST... *OOMF* RUN ALONG AND HAVE FUN!
OH!
SORRY, DIDN'T SEE YOU DOWN THERE!
NO PROBLEM! JUST TRYING OUT A NEW POINT OF VIEW.
I'M ZACK. I HAVEN'T SEEN YOU AROUND BEFORE, YOU MUST GO TO A DIFFERENT SCHOOL.
I'M BLYTHE! ACTUALLY, GO TO—UM
HEY GUYS, THIS IS BLYTHE!
BLYTHE, MEET RHONDA, TAMMY, AND SCOTT.
HEY THERE!
WHAT'S UP?
OOO, I LOVE YOUR HAT, TAMMY!
THANKS! I MADE IT MYSELF. I SEW ALL MY OWN CLOTHES WITH SUSTAINABLE FABRICS.
COOL!

FIDDLESTICKS!!
IS THAT SAFE? OR LEGAL?
WE ALL TWIST THE WORLD INTO WHAT WE WANT IT TO BE, RUSSELL. WE ALL DO.
MUSIC IS WHAT PUTS EVERYTHING RIGHT AGAIN.
OH! OH! I HEAR A SONG AND MY DANCING FEET JUST HAVE TO BE FREE!
TAP TAP TAP TAP TAP
HERE I GO!
MEE-MEE-MEE-MEE...
HAROOOOOOW
EEEEYERK
TWANG TAP TAP
TINK TINK
CHING CHING
TWING
HOWLOOOOO
HAROOOOOOW

HEY, MARTIN! CHECK THIS OUT!
IT'S LIKE I TOOK A CHEESE GRATER AND SCRAPED IT ON A CHALK BOARD WHILE MY CAT YERFED A HAIRBALL.
ISN'T THAT LIKE, THE WORST SOUND EVER?
I LOVE IT IRONICALLY!
THIS HEAT IS SERIOUSLY DAMAGING MY BEAUTIFUL VOCALS.
CHA-CHING
HAMBU
YOUR SOUND IS KILLER! ARE YOU GUYS SOME KIND OF PERFORMANCE ART THING?
WE ARE NOW!
LET'S SPRUCE UP THIS AMATEUR ACT AND GO PRO!

I HAD SO MUCH FUN TODAY! AND NOW I CAN ACTUALLY SAY I'VE PLAYED BONGOS.
WE'LL SEE YOU TOMORROW!
G'NIGHT!
HERE—I BROUGHT SOME CLOTHES YOU CAN BORROW.
OH! YOU DON'T HAVE TO DO THAT!
YOU LIKED MY HAT SO MUCH AND THESE ARE JUST A LITTLE LESS UPTIGHT. YOU KNOW WHAT I'M SAYING?
OH!
HI, BLYTHE! WHAT DID YOU KEEP YOURSELF SO BUSY WITH TODAY?
I MADE SOME NEW FRIENDS.
GOOD FOR YOU!
LESS TALK, MORE BEDTIME. I'M *EXHAUSTED.*
I LIKE ALL OF YOU, BUT NOT AS MUCH THIS CLOSE.
HUH.
WHEN YOU PUT THIS MANY FEET IN ONE PLACE IT'S ALMOST AS IF THEY DON'T STINK ANYMORE!
ALMOST.

THE NEXT MORNING—
HERE GOES...
GOOD MORNING!
HEY, BLYTHE! LOVE THE THREADS.
WE'RE GOING TO VOLUNTEER FOR THE "HANDS ACROSS THE WORLD" ART INSTALLATION TONIGHT. WANT TO COME?
I'D LOVE TO, THAT SOUNDS LIK A BLAST!
BRITTANY, DID YOU LIKE, KNOW THERE WAS A FESTIVAL THING GOING ON TODAY?
LIKE, I WOULDN'T HAVE COME TO THE BEACH IF I DID? IT'S CRAWLING WITH "PEACE & LOVE" AND WHATEVER.
IF WE HADN'T PUT SO MUCH EFFORT INTO GETTING HERE WE'D TOTALLY BE DITCHING THIS PLACE.
YEAH, WHITTANY.
I MEAN, I KNOW FRANCOIS PACKED OUR STUFF AND DROVE US HERE AND DID ALL THE WORK, BUT STILL.

HEY, RHONDA! CHECK OUT THE REALITY SHOW WANNA-BE'S.
THE BISKIT TWINS?
DO YOU THINK THEY'VE EVER HAD A THOUGHT IN THEIR HEAD THEIR DADDY DIDN'T BUY FOR THEM?
HA HA!
SNICKER
IT ISN'T SO GREAT TO MAKE FUN OF PEOPLE. BRITTANY AND WHITTANY AREN'T THAT BAD.
ARE THEY FRIENDS OF YOURS?
WELL, NO... NOT FRIENDS, EXACTLY.
THAT'S A RELIEF. I DIDN'T THINK YOU WERE THE TYPE TO HANG OUT WITH THE ENTITLEMENT CROWD.
I TOLD YOU SHE'S COOL.
SO, DO YOU THINK THEIR FEET TOUCHED THE SAND OR DID THEIR BUTLER ROLL OUT A RED CARPET TO PROTECT THEIR DELICATE SKIN?
I'M GOING TO GET A WATER.

MEANWHILE...
THE CONCERT IS TONIGHT, WE NEED TO PULL THIS TRACK TOGETHER!
SORRY, SUNIL. I THINK I MISSED A NOTE ON THE SECOND CHORUS.
I GET THAT WE'RE TRYING TO BE CHILL AND ALL, BUT WE ALL *KNOW* WHO'S MESSING UP.
I HOPE YOU'RE NOT SUGGESTING THAT *I'M* IN ANY WAY TO BLAME.
I HAVE *PERFECT* PITCH!
I WOULD SUGGEST THAT, BUT POINTING PAWS IS TOTALLY NOT ZEN.
THAT STILL SOUNDS LIKE YOU'RE SAYING IT'S ME. IS SHE SAYING IT'S ME?
SORRY I'M LATE FOR PRACTICE...
AW MAN, AM I IN THE WRONG ERA AGAIN?

BLINK BLINK
I DREAMED I WAS IN A COOL DYSFUNCTIONAL BAND AND YOU TOTALLY RUINED IT, VINNIE.
THAT SOUNDS LIKE ME.
I'M JUST SAYING YOU'RE A TEENSY-WEENY BIT FLAT.
AND I'M JUST SAYING YOU'RE A TEENSY-WEENY BIT WRONG!
NOW I REMEMBER. I'M IN AN UNCOOL DYSFUNCTIONAL BAND.
DO I *HAVE* TO BE THE TAMBOURINE PLAYER? NO ONE RESPECTS THE TAMBOURINE PLAYER.
STOP!
I KNOW WHAT WE NEED TO BRING THIS BAND TOGETHER.
BLYTHE!

HEY, PENNY LING! WHAT'S THE MATTER?
OUR BAND NEEDS YOUR HELP!
YOU HAVE A BAND?
SURE DO! WE GOT TONS OF TIPS YESTERDAY.
MRS. TWOMBLY IS GOING TO USE THE MONEY TO MAKE A BIG DONATION TO THE PET SHELTER.
WELL, IT IS A REALLY GOOD CAUSE... THOUGH I DID HAVE THIS ART INSTALLATION THING TO GO TO...
LET'S GET TO WORK.

WE SHOULD TRY PENNY LING ON THE TAMBOURINE... PEPPER, YOU CAN BE BACKUP PERCUSSION—
THERE YOU ARE, BLYTHE!
WE WERE WONDERING WHAT HAPPENED TO YOU.
OH! HI, GUYS. I WAS JUST... UM...
ARE YOU... TRAINING ANIMALS TO PLAY INSTRUMENTS?
I DON'T KNOW, BLYTHE. THAT SEEMS KIND OF LAME.
LET'S GO HANG OUT AND RELAX. LET PETS BE PETS, OK?
UH, YEAH... OK...
NO.
WE WERE HAVING FUN UNTIL YOU TRIED TO MAKE ME FEEL BAD.
YOU THINK YOU'RE SO EASY-GOING, BUT YOU REALLY ONLY LIKE PEOPLE WHO ACT EXACTLY LIKE YOU DO.

I'M STAYING AND I DON'T CARE HOW LAME THAT MAKES ME.
IF THAT'S THE WAY YOU WANT IT.
GUESS I WAS WRONG ABOUT YOU AFTER ALL.
I'M SO SORRY, BLYTHE.
YOU DIDN'T HAVE TO GIVE UP YOUR FRIENDS JUST FOR US.
IT'S OK.
REAL FRIENDS WOULDN'T ASK ME TO CHANGE.
I KNOW THIS WASN'T WHAT I WAS PLANNING TO DO THIS WEEK—
BUT I'D RATHER BE HERE WITH YOU AND THE PETS THAN ANYWHERE ELSE IN TOWN!
HAROOOOOOW
EEEEYERK
THAT IS SO SWEET, BLYTHE!
WE'LL SEE IF YOU STILL FEEL THAT WAY IN A COUPLE OF HOURS.

KEEP COOL, SUNIL! THEY'RE NOT REAL SNAKES!
MIXED NUTS

I'M VERY IMPRESSED WITH HOW MANY RESPONSES CAME IN FOR MY FIRST-EVER "LITTLEST PET SHOP CUSTOMER SATISFACTION SURVEY."
PEOPLE LOVE TO HAVE OPINIONS, MRS. TWOMBLY.
HE BRACING RACE
Georgia Ball
Nico Peña
Victoria Robado
Tom B. Long
EVERYONE THINKS YOUR PET FASHIONS ARE THE BEE'S KNEES, BLYTHE.
I'LL TAKE THAT AS A COMPLIMENT.
BUT I GOT SEVERAL COMPLAINTS THAT THE PETS DON'T LOOK VERY "EXERCISED."
WHAT THE—HUH?

MAYBE THE PETS HAVE GOTTEN TOO COMFORTABLE.
I'LL HAVE A CHAT—ER, I MEAN... I'LL CHECK IN ON THEM AND SEE WHAT I CAN DO.
OOO! I KNOW THIS JINGLE— WACKADOODLE SWAB & SALAD SLICERS™!
HEH HEH... IT CUTS YOUR ONIONS AND CLEANS YOUR EARS.
THE PEOPLE IN THESE ADS CAN'T OPEN A CUPBOARD OR CARRY A GARBAGE BAG WITHOUT HURTING THEMSELVES.
HOW DID THEY SURVIVE THIS LONG WITH-OUT BASIC LIFE SKILLS?
ARE YOU GUYS WATCHIN INFOMERCIAL FOR FUN?
IT'S CALLED "EDUTAINMENT."
WELL, I'VE GOT A BETTER IDEA. WHO WANTS TO PLAY A GAME?

I THINK
HAT WOULD
ERFERE WITH
Y PLAN TO
AROUND AND
RATCH THE
ACK OF MY
EAD TODAY.
A CLUEMASTER SENDS US TO A LOCATION, WE SOLVE A RIDDLE...
AND THE FIRST TEAM TO TAKE A PICTURE OF THE ITEM WE'RE LOOKING FOR GETS A POINT. JUST BORROW MY PHONE WHEN YOU SEE THE ANSWER!
THIS BOX OF "BACON LOVIN' PET ENERGY BARS" GOES TO THE FIRST TEAM THAT SOLVES A CLUE IN TWO LOCATIONS.
I'LL BE THE CLUEMASTER! THE MASTERMIND WORKING BEHIND THE SCENES...
THE PUPPETEER PULLING THE STRINGS...
DANCE, PUPPETS, DANCE!
UH...
...PENNY LING WILL STAY AND HELP RUSSELL.
EVERYONE
E, PICK YOUR
MMATE FROM
THE JAR.
DON'T LET THIS GO TO HIS HEAD.
NO WORRIES. I'M GOOD AT THAT.

GOOD LUCK, GUYS!
AS CLUEMASTER, I'LL CHOOSE THE LOCATIONS, WHILE YOU WRITE THE CLUES.
WHOOOOOOSSSH
WELL, THAT WAS A *LOVELY* OUTING.
LET'S DO IT AGAIN SOMETIME.
WE'RE *NOT* GIVING UP THAT EASY, ZOE.
WE'LL JUST STICK TO INDOOR LOCATIONS.
WE STILL HAVE TO GET THERE.
ARRGH!! WHAT IS THE POINT OF A PUPPY PONCHO IF THE WATER SPLASHES UP UNDER IT?!

WE'VE ALMOST REACHED OUR FIRST LOCATION.
RUSSELL KNOWS THE PARK IS NOT INDOORS, RIGHT?
BECAUSE IT'S TOTALLY NOT.
THEY'RE ALMOST AT THE ARK RECREATION ENTER... IS THE CLUE READY YET?
YOU SHOULDN'T RUSH ART, RUSSELL.
BUT, YES, IT'S HERE ON MY DESK
THANKS, PENNY! I'LL JUST LEAVE THE PRIZE NEXT TO YOU.
I DON'T THINK I CAN RESIST THE TEMPTATION TO SNACK ON IT.
HERE'S THE FIRST CLUE...
"CONSIDER THE USES THIS TOOL ENTAILS..."
"IT MAY BE A HAMMER, BUT IT'S NOT FOR NAILS."

C'MON, VINNIE. TEAM "LIZARD BREATH" IS GONNA WIN THIS THING!
ZOE? WHERE IS ZOE?
I'M SO HAPPY I'M ON YOUR TEEEEEAM!!!
Downtown City Rock & Gem Club
MINKA...
YOU LOOK LIKE SOMEONE WHO WOULD BE INTERESTED IN LEARNING MORE ABOUT THE EXCITING WORLD OF ROCKS.
I DO?
DID YOU KNOW THAT COLLECTING ROCKS HAS MANY PRACTICAL USES?
FOR INSTANCE, YOU CAN PUT THEM ON YOUR SHELF. YOU CAN ALSO LOOK AT YOUR ROCKS.
THE TOOLS OF A ROCK HOUND INCLUDE PICKS, TUMBLERS...
WAIT—TOOLS! DO YOU USE ANYTHING THA LOOKS LIKE A HAMMER?
ZZZZZZZ
THE CHISEL POINT ROCK HAMMER IS A VITAL TOOL IN THE ROCK HOUND'S ARSENAL.
SOME MIGHT THINK ALL TOOLS THAT BREAK ROCKS ARE ALIKE, BUT THEY WOULD BE WRONG.
CLICK
GASP THAT'S EXACTLY WHAT *I'VE* BEEN SAYING!
AND WE HAVE A WINNER! FIRST POINT GOES TO TEAM MONKEY-BRAINS.

THIS ROUND'S OVER, EVERYBODY! WE'RE MOVING ON.
ALREADY???
I CAN'T BELIEVE I FOUND YOU FLIRTING WITH A SERVICE DOG.
GIGGLE I SEE A CANINE IN UNIFORM AND I JUST MELT.
OK, BLYTHE... YOUR NEXT LOCATION IS THE ZEN CAFE. THE WEBSITE SAYS THEY'RE "PET-FRIENDLY."
WE NEED THAT NEXT CLUE, PRONTO!
UNH! TOO MUCH PRESSURE!
IF ONLY THERE WAS SOMETHING I COULD DO TO RELIEVE THE STRESS...

"WHAT HAS A SMILE AND SMELLS LIKE HOME? JUST LOOK FOR A FRIENDLY FACE IN THE FOAM!"
YECH. THESE CLUES ARE SO CUTESY-WOOTSY.
THINK! WHAT HAS A FACE AND A SMELL?
I'M NOT SURE YOU REALLY WANT ME TO ANSWER THAT.
LOOK, VINNIE!
WE'RE ALREADY A POINT BEHIND. IF WE DON'T STEP UP OUR GAME, WE'RE GOING TO GET SKUNKED.
WHOA THERE, PEPPER. WHAT WAS IN YOUR WHEATIE-O'S THIS MORNING?
BREAKFAST... COFFEE! INGENIOUS!!
CAN I TAKE A PICTURE OF YOUR "LATTE ART"? YOU'RE THE BEST!
CLICK
POINT GOES TO LIZARD BREAT
HOW DID YOU FIGUR
IT OUT SO FAST?
I WAS HIGHLY MOTIVATED.

YOU'LL FIND THE NEXT LOCATION AT THE CORNER OF 4TH AND MADISON.
DOES IT HAVE TO BE POSH?
THIS STORE IS SO EXPENSIVE THEY MIGHT CHARGE ME FOR BREATHING THEIR AIR.
BLECH!!
WOOOOSH
AAND NOW I'M A WET MESS.
ANYWAY, THE CLUE IS "PLOP AND IT EXPLODES WITH FIZZ; IT DETONATES BUT DOESN'T TICK!"
HEY, BRITTANY... IS THAT LIKE, BLYTHE? SHE'S TOTALLY STANDING INSIDE OF POSH.
WHITTANY, I'M LIKE, SO GLAD YOU SAID THAT? FOR A SECOND, I THOUGHT WE WERE AT THE WRONG STORE.

AND THE BISKITS ARE HERE. YAY...
SO, *BLYTHE...* ARE YOU TRYING TO IMAGINE WHAT IT WOULD BE LIKE TO BE TRENDY ENOUGH TO WEAR THESE CLOTHES?
OF COURSE, WE ONLY SHOP AT POSH WHEN WE'RE LOOKING FOR A BARGAIN.
THEY DON'T EVEN CHARGE EXTRA FOR YOUR RECEIPT!
HA HA! I LO EVERYTHIN ABOUT TH STORE, JUS DON'T LOO OVER THER
SSSHIIIIINNNY!
WE'RE GOING TO FOCUS ON THE GAME THIS TIME, RIGHT, ZOE? RIGHT?
OK! WELL, I'LL LET YOU TWO GET BACK TO BUYING $500 TOOTHPICKS OR WHATEVER.
TOOTHPICKS ARE ON SALE??
I JUST WENT TO THE POSH WEBSITE AND *TOTALLY* BOUGHT ONE.
TAP TAP TAP TAP
YOU'RE SO SMART, BRITTANY. WE WOULD HAVE HAD TO WALK ALL THE WAY TO THE NEXT ROOM TO BUY ONE HERE.

I FOUND IT!
FOUND WHAT? DID YOU SOLVE THE CLUE? WHAT DID YOU FIND?
SUNIL, LOOK AT THIS *GORGEOUS* TUNIC BY DONNA VERSASHA-ARMANA ST. DIOR!
ISN'T IT *DIVINE*?
ZOE, YOU'RE A SPANIEL! WHY DO YOU *CARE* ABOUT HUMAN CLOTHES?
ACTUALLY IT IS KIND OF NICE. IS THAT CHAMBRAY?
I TOLD YOU THIS WAS THE WRONG SECTION, VINNY. CLOTHES DON'T EXPLODE!
TONE DOWN THE SCENT, PEPPER. I'M TRYING TO CONCENTRATE.
YOU NEVER LISTEN! THIS IS JUST LIKE THE TIME I TOLD YOU NOT TO EAT FLIES WHILE THEY'RE STILL ON THE PAPER.
YOU REALLY NEED TO STOP BRINGING THAT UP.
IT TOOK US HOURS TO GET THAT STUFF OFF YOUR TONGUE!
SHINY SHINY SHINY SHINY SHINY

WOO KEEE KEEE KEEEAWK AWK AWK
EEP EEP
TINK
I LIKE TO THINK THAT TASTE IS A UNIVERSAL TRUTH THAT APPLIES TO *ANY* SPECIES—
WHOOOOSH
EEEK EEEK EEEK EEEK
GOODNESS, MINKA! THAT EXPLOSION OF ACTIVITY NEARLY TUSSLED MY HAIR...
GASP I KNOW THE ANSWER! *A BOMB!*
A *BATH* BOMB TO BE EXACT!
RUFF RUFF RUFF
WE GOT A POINT! I CAN'T BELIEVE IT.
THE MORE I KNOW ABOUT BLYTHE'S LIFESTYLE—
LIKE, THE LESS I WANT TO KNOW.

ALL THREE TEAMS HAVE A POINT, RUSSELL.
WE NEED A TIEBREAKER RIGHT AWAY.
NOW? ER, OK... I'LL TALK TO PENNY.
RR RAWR ROWL RUNT RUNT GRRRRRR
UH, RUSSELL? IS EVERYTHING OK?
ULP... YOUR NEXT LOCATION IS—UM... I'LL TEXT YOU AN ADDRESS.
WAIT A MINUTE... THIS IS THE ADDRESS FOR—

"SUE'S PLACE."
THANKS FOR STOPPING BY, BLYTHE. IT WAS A REALLY, *REALLY* BIG SURPRISE!
YEAH, SUE... IT SURE WAS!
AND YOU BROUGHT SO MANY OF THE PETS!
SO *MANY* OF THEM.
YOUR FRIEND IS OUT OF CHIPS.
CUTE! HIS BODY LANGUAGE IS ALL "HEY BABE, GET ME SOME CHIPS" BUT HIS VOICE IS ALL "*SQUEAK-SQUEE-SQUEAK!*"
EXCUSE ME, I NEED TO MAKE A PHONE CALL.
AW, HE THINKS HE'S PEOPLE.
RUSSELL, WHAT'S GOING ON? ARE WE SUPPOSED TO BE LOOKING FOR SOMETHING AT SUE'S HOUSE?
UM, WE'RE HAVING SOME TECHNICAL DIFFICULTIES. JUST HANG TIGHT, BLYTHE.

O WAS THAT THE PHONE? I RD GRUNTING NOISES...
THAT WAS—MY DAD! HE HAS A COLD. HE WANTS ME TO GET BACK RIGHT AWAY SO I CAN GIVE HIM HIS MEDS.
SUCH A BABY.
WELL, THAT WAS FUN. SO LONG, SUE. THANKS FOR HAVING US!
I THINK THERE'S SOMETHING RUSSELL ISN'T TELLING ME.
DON'T FRET, PENNY. I STALLED HEM, WE HAVE PLENTY OF TIME TO—
—GET BUSTED.

ALL RIGHT, RUSSELL, WHAT ARE YOU HIDING? SPILL IT!
WELL... UH... IT'S THE CRAZIEST THING—
IT'S MY FAULT, BLYTHE. WE DIDN'T KNOW WHAT TO DO NEXT BECAUSE...
I KIND OF ATE THE PRIZE.
ERP
WE'RE SORRY WE SENT YOU ALL OVER DOWNTOWN CITY FOR NO REASON! WHAT CAN WE DO TO MAKE IT UP TO YOU?!
I HAVE A SUGGESTION.
MY TUMMY HURTS.
OOPS, SORRY PENNY... DULL, ORDINARY KNIVES CAN'T SEEM TO CUT ANYTHING RIGHT.
THREE MORE TAKES AND WE'LL START RECORDING.
NOW THIS I
EDUTAINMEN
NICELY DONE! I AM ALMOST CONVINCED HE IS MISSING THE BASIC SKILLS REQUIRED TO CUT WITH A KNIFE.

a rockin' father's day
Written by Matt Anderson
Art by Antonio Campo
Colors by Diego Rodriguez
Letters by Tom B. Long
Edits by David Hedgecock
BLYTHE, DEAR. I JUST HAVE ONE QUESTION FOR YOU.
ARE YOU READY TO...
...RRRAAAAWWWK?!?!?!
WEEEOOOO WWEEEOOO!
ACTUALLY...
IT DOESN'T MATTER IF YOU'RE READY OR NOT, BECAUSE WE GOTTA HIT THE ROAD. I DON'T WANT TO MISS A SECOND OF THE CONCERT.

I JUST NEED ANOTHER MINUTE, DAD. I'M HAVING TROUBLE DECIDING WHICH SHIRT TO WEAR.
IS THAT SO? WELL, PROBLEM *SOLVED*.
HUH?
OH...
I BOUGHT THAT SHIRT AT COILED COUSIN'S FAREWELL CONCERT BACK WHEN I WAS IN HIGH SCHOOL.
OBVIOUSLY, IT'S TOO SMALL FOR ME TO WEAR THESE DAYS, BELIEVE ME I *JUST TRIED.* BUT I WAS THINKING IT WOULD BE PRETTY *RADICAL* IF YOU WORE IT TONIGHT.
COILED COUSIN
WHAT DO *YOU* THINK?
YEAH...
...RADICAL.

the Chord
ED COUSIN
NION TOUR
SOLD OUT!
I CAN NOT BELIEVE WE ARE LESS THAN THREE, ACCOUNTING FOR THE OPENING BANDS, HOURS FROM SEEING...
...THE COUSIN.
THAT'S WHAT US REAL FANS CALL COILED COUSIN.
CLEVER.
THIS IS...
...THE BEST FATHER'S DAY GIFT EVER!
YEAH...YOU KNOW...IT'S FUNNY, WHEN I GOT YOU THE TICKETS I WAS UNDER THE IMPRESSION THAT YOU WERE GOING TO BRING A FRIEND.
I DID.
THE BEST FRIEND EVER!
BLYTHE?

ARE YOU GOING TO THE COILED COUSIN CONCERT?
UMM... I... I GUESS—
THAT'S AWESOME!
YOU'RE A FAN?
YEP. THE COUSIN IS GREAT! THEY'RE TOTALLY RETRO.
MY DAD GOT ME INTO THEM. I WAS HOPING HE WAS GOING TO COME TO THE SHOW WITH ME, BUT HE SAYS HE'S "TOO OLD" FOR CONCERTS.
I GUESS HE'S NOT AS COOL AS YOUR DAD.
NOT TO SOUND BRAGGY, BUT MY DAD IS PRETTY HARD TO BEAT IN A COOL COMPETITION.
RIGHT ON.
I BETTER GO GET IN LINE. I'LL LOOK FOR YOU INSIDE.
OH, I ALMOST FORGOT, THAT'S AN AWESOME SHIRT!
IT'S RADICAL.
YOU'RE RADICAL.
End.

LOOK GUYS, IT'S REAL SIMPLE. JUST DO WHAT I DO.
SO YOU THINK YOU CAN DANCE CRAZE?
Written by Matt Anderson
Art by Antonio Campo
Colors by Diego Rodriguez
Letters by Tom B. Long
Edits by David Hedgecock
LOVE
ARM OUT.
GOOD.
ARM UP.
NOW, WE BUILD ON THOSE WITH...
EXCELLENT. YOU GOT THE FUNDAMENTALS.

...THIS!
SEE? NOTHING TO IT.
IT'S A GUARANTEED HIT!
SURE TO SWEEP THE NATION. DON'T YOU AGREE?
UM... I'M AFRAID TO SAY THAT YOU LOST US...
...AGAIN.

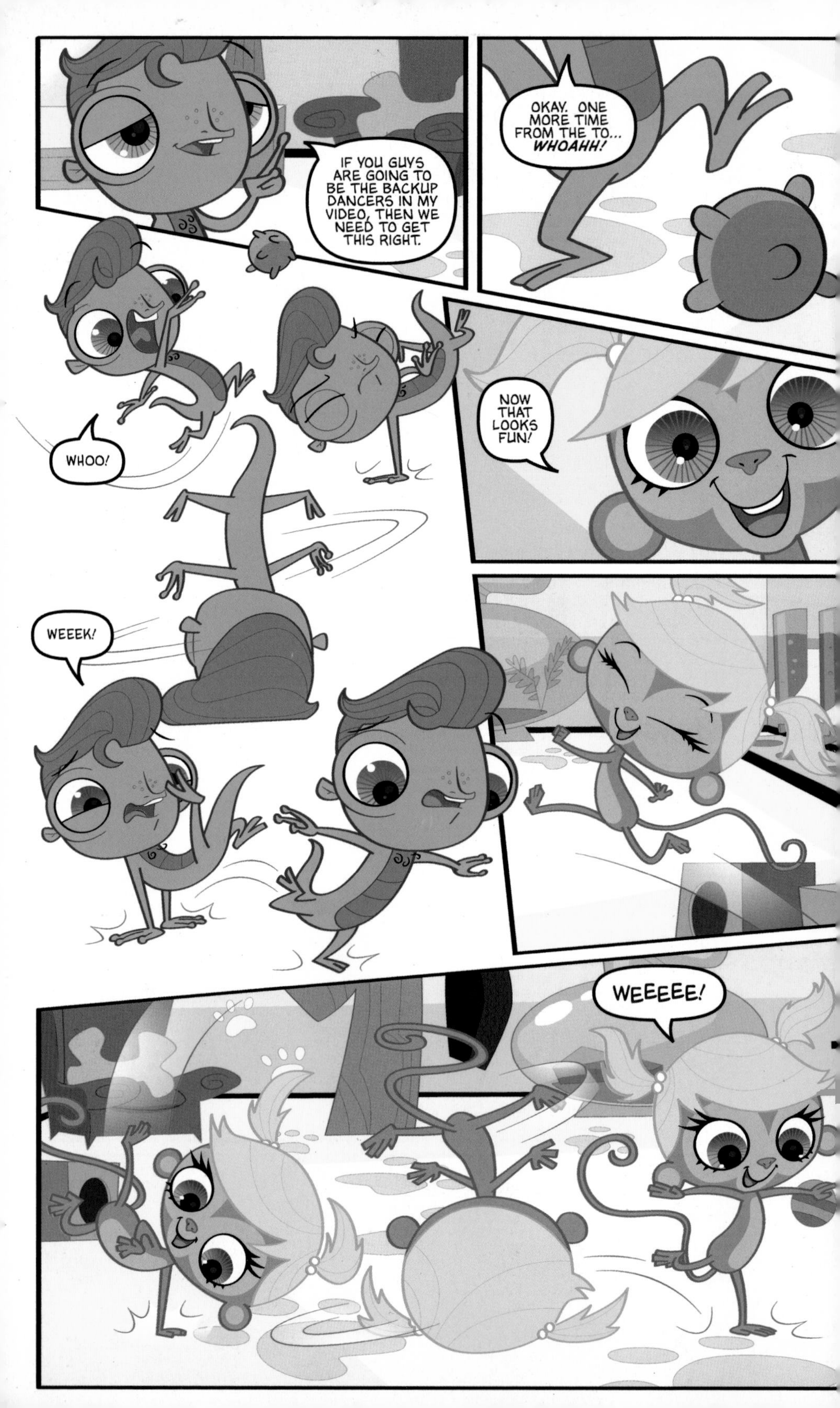
IF YOU GUYS ARE GOING TO BE THE BACKUP DANCERS IN MY VIDEO, THEN WE NEED TO GET THIS RIGHT.
OKAY. ONE MORE TIME FROM THE TO... *WHOAHH!*
WHOO!
NOW THAT LOOKS FUN!
WEEEK!
WEEEEE!

WOO
WEE
WOO
WHAT IN THE WORLD IS GOING ON HERE?
WE'RE DANCING!
OOOOKAY...
WEE
WOO WEE
WOO WEE
WOO
End.

A FINE DAY FOR A PARADE
Written by Matt Anderson
Art by Antonio Campo
Colors by Victoria Robado
Letters by Tom B. Long
Edits by David Hedgecock
DOWNTOWN CITY'S ANNUAL CELEBRATORY PARADE.
WHITTANY! BRITTANY! PAY ATTENTION TO THE CROWD!
UGH. DO WE HAVE TO DO, LIKE, EVERYTHING?
RIGHT. I MEAN, HELLO, WE'RE HERE. THEY CAN SEE US. ISN'T THAT ENOUGH?

Littlest Pet Shop
THE BISKITS HAVE THE BIGGEST FLOAT HERE AND...
...IT'S *NO FUN AT ALL*. THEY'RE *RUINING* THE PARADE.
"NO FUN"?
NO ONE *RUINS* A PARADE ON *MY* WATCH!

I JUST GOT YOUR TEXT ABOUT HOW LAME THIS PARADE IS. YOU ARE SO FUNNY, BRITTANY.
AND I JUST GOT YOUR TEXT ABOUT HOW BORING THIS PARADE IS. IT CRACKED ME UP, WHITTANY.
WE'RE BOTH FUNNY.
I KNOW, RIGHT.
AHHH! IT'S A GRIZZLY BEAR!
YAAAY!
WOO HOO!
WHAT THE HUH?
YAY!
WOO-HOO! GO PENNY!
WOO HOO!

YAAAY!
WOO HOO!
YAAY!
WOO HOO!
WOO HOO!
NOW THAT'S HOW YOU BRING THE FUN!
End.

ALSO AVAILABLE!
Littlest Pet Shop™
CEREAL
OPEN FOR BUSINESS
IDW
Littlest Pet Shop: Open For Busi
HC ISBN: 978-1-63140-
SC ISBN: 978-1-63140-